Be Your Own Best Friend

First published in 2017 by
The Better Life Project
Dublin, Ireland

ISBN 978-1-9998897-0-8

Editor: Kezia Bayard-White
Interior book design: Rebecca Souster
Cover design: White Bear Studio

Printed and bound in Great Britain

Be Your Own Best Friend

A DAILY JOURNAL FOR WOMEN FOR BUILDING SELF-ESTEEM AND USING COMPASSION IN EVERYDAY LIFE

Sarah Doyle

the better life project

Contents

Practical Exercises

The 12-Week Journal

Dear B,

It's time to start. P is for progress, not perfect. I've got your back.

Lots of love,

Sarah

X

Be Your Own Best Friend

How to Use This Journal

This is the most important (and fabulous) journal you own!

Be Your Own Best Friend was created to help you care for and nurture the most important person in your life – you!

Using proven positive psychology principles, such as self-compassion, gratitude, optimism and many more, this journal will provide space for you to nurture your self-esteem and learn how you can use compassion in your everyday life. *Be Your Own Best Friend* uses inspiring affirmations, daily prompts, activities and positive self-reflection to help you find your sparkle again. All of this will be done in small, simple steps. I have also included some really practical and helpful exercises to help you protect and build your self-esteem and confidence.

Setbacks and bad days are a part of life. Even though we can't change what they are, we can control how we respond to them. These exercises are your tools for life!

All too often we get caught up in negative thoughts and actions that can spiral out of control and cause us to feel bad about ourselves. *Be Your Own Best Friend* will help you record meaningful moments so that you learn to focus your thoughts and energy on the positive things in life.

Designed to be used for a 12-week period, each page has been beautifully created to help you nurture your most fabulous relationship: the one you have with yourself! Every page corresponds to a new day and includes up to three questions carefully crafted to help you focus your thoughts in a positive way and develop a deep understanding and appreciation for yourself – warts and all!

Day 6 of *Be Your Own Best Friend* is your Day of Compassion and is your reminder to treat yourself with a positive attitude. Day 7 is your Weekly Check-in. This weekly check-in uses gratitude and hope-building exercises to help you stay committed and accountable whilst creating even more space for you to learn about yourself and reflect on your week with positivity and a deeper sense of resilience.

By using self-awareness and compassion, I want to show you how it is possible to develop a strong sense of self and learn how you can accept and love your mind, body and spirit.

At times it may feel like quite the challenge to answer these questions and I want you to know that this is 100% OK and normal. Please don't give up on yourself if you start to struggle. Instead, you might like to try a couple of things to help:

- *Laugh* – put on a funny clip on YouTube, your favourite episode of Friends or your all-time favourite comedian, and giggle. This dose of endorphins might be the natural high you need to help you answer these questions.

- *Breathe* – go outside for a walk and, if you want, take your journal with you. When outside take measured and deliberate breaths to help ease your anxiety and keep you grounded.

- *Take it slow* – try one question at a time or take five minutes to answer just one question a day.

You are enough, and you are doing a brilliant job so far, so please don't forget that.

Together, we will embark on this journey to a deeper appreciation, acceptance and love for yourself. Using focussed questions to help you develop your self-esteem, whilst understanding ways to practice self-compassion in everyday life, I want to show you how it is possible to become your own best friend.

A Note from Sarah

I have failed, made mistakes, felt humiliated and foolish. I have been called fat by boys and girls have made fun of me. I have been rejected, laughed at and judged.

But nothing, and I mean nothing, has been more hurtful, degrading or painful as the things that I have said to myself – the thoughts I have played on repeat, over and over again in my mind.

I, single-handedly, shattered my self-esteem, and unlike a ripped dress or chipped nail varnish, I had no idea how to put myself back together. I gave myself such a hard time, all the time. But I was always someone else's best friend.

My friends would come to me for support and I would shower them with unconditional love and kindness. I would hold a safe space for them to grieve, cry, shout, moan, and then together, we would brainstorm solutions and search for a silver lining. I was their cheerleader, wingman, life coach and best friend.

But I only ever offered myself criticism and cruelty. I was my worst enemy and toughest critic. I would beat myself up whenever I would say the wrong thing or make a mistake. If sweating the small stuff was in the Olympics I would have won! When something positive happened in my life I would brush it under the rug or feel completely undeserving. But if something negative would happen I would grab a cup of tea, sit on the couch and obsessively think and rethink every detail!

The pressure I put on myself to be accepted, the best, or someone's favourite, was the root cause of so much sadness, anxiety and stress in my life. I was bulimic for over 10 years and I still suffer from occasional bouts of appearance-related anxiety. I used to compare myself to everyone and everything around me, and I would feel completely wired when I got stressed or anxious. Sometimes the voices in my head made me feel like I was broken. But then, I learned how to be my own best friend.

Be Your Own Best Friend is for all of you that feel the pressure and judgement of others, but face the most criticism from yourself. I want to show you that you are not broken and that you do not need to be fixed. You are, and always have been, enough. I want to show you how you can become your own best friend, just like I did. It won't always be easy but it will be worth it.

My name is Sarah and this journal will guide you to become your own best friend.

A Lesson in Self-Esteem

No other self-help topic has generated as much advice and as many explanations as self-esteem.

So let's set the record straight!

Self-esteem refers to your own feelings of worth or value. It is a judgement of your own life – your relationship with yourself. When we do things that we enjoy that make us feel accomplished and happy with our lives, we feel good generally. Building self-esteem in the right way can be an incredibly rewarding journey for women. However, finding the 'right way' to build self-esteem is often more of a problem than whether we have it or not to begin with.

Have you ever snapped at your kids because you were exhausted, fallen short of hitting your targets at work, or had an off day in the gym, and then felt terrible about yourself because you usually do these things so well? These setbacks or mistakes are often used to help us understand if we are a 'good' or a 'bad' person. When we use our previous successes and accomplishments as the key to unlock our self-esteem we eventually create such high expectations that it is impossible to meet these standards all of the time. Contingent self-esteem is self-esteem based on the approval of others, or on social comparisons[1], and this is something that we need to be conscious of. How can we feel good about ourselves without needing to feel better than others or constantly striving for better than yesterday?

We are, at the end of the day, imperfect beings and 'bad' days are just a part of life.

Contingent self-esteem will manifest in many ways and I am sure you can relate to some of these; excessive self-consciousness and self-criticism of your appearance, the pressure of trying to be perfect, people pleasing or the fear of being judged and maybe a little social anxiety.

Life can be tough! We will make mistakes and things won't always go the way we planned. By learning to shift your focus inward and to use self-compassion in everyday life you can avoid the self-esteem trap I fell into on so many occasions; only enjoying exercise if I was good at it, only feeling good about my body if it looked 'perfect' and only valuing my work if others valued it. The list could go on.

My inner critic can pack a serious punch but self-compassion was my pathway to a happier and more fulfilled life.

But remember, happiness is not about trying to eliminate all the negativity from our life and being an optimist does not mean that you will never have moments of despair, anxiety and discouragement. It means that you never let these thoughts take over your life.

It will be difficult to grow and develop into the woman you want to become, if you struggle accepting the woman you already are. Your personal growth journey will begin with self-awareness and self-acceptance. A journey that you, with this journal in hand, have already begun.

1. Neff, K (2011) *Self-Compassion*. London: Hodder and Stoughton

“

Caring for myself isn't self-indulgent, it is self-preservation. It won't always be exciting, easy or fun but it is always worth it.

”

A Lesson in Self-Compassion

Self-compassion involves being kind to ourselves when life doesn't go the way we planned, or when we notice something about ourselves we don't like.

How we respond to ourselves in our moments of perceived inadequacy, failure, or general suffering, will make us or break us. Self-compassion recognises that the human condition is imperfect. Life has been made of up of imperfect moments; perfect will never rescue us in our moments of pain and suffering.

Imagine a friend struggling with life, feeling stressed, sad and just plain shitty. Imagine she comes to you for love and support and all you do is criticise, insult and judge her. Even though your friend has suffered a significant and upsetting setback, you make it worse. Whether you mean to or not!

Imagine your child at the start of a 50m dash for her school's sports day. She's feeling nervous and self-conscious but the whistle blows and she gets off to a great start. However, just before the finish line she trips and falls. You can see tears prickle in her eyes and your face start to redden as you can sense her disappointment and sadness. You expect her to stand up, all on her own, but when she turns to you for encouragement all you do is whisper 'failure' and walk away.

Would you do this? I hope not.

I bet you would you provide your friend with unconditional kindness, non-judgemental listening and a positive attitude. You would listen, brainstorm solutions and give her a pep talk.

And your daughter, you would embrace her in your arms and kiss away her tears. You would pick her up and run by her side to the finish line.

Why should *you* be any different? Why are *you* the exception to your own rule?

You are no different! You are worthy of this love and kindness too.

Self-compassion is about treating yourself like you would your best friend, daughter, son and loved one.

Self-esteem will be the bricks you use to rebuild your life, self-compassion will be the cement holding it all together.

Practical Exercises

Quietening your Inner Mean Girl Voice

You know that inner voice that often whispers, or maybe shouts, 'You aren't enough, you can't do this, who do you think you are? Well this is your inner critic, also called your inner mean girl voice. It is something that we all have in varying degrees and is there, whether you like it or not. My inner critic is called Lazy Bum Bum Face, or B for short, and she can pack a serious punch.

For me, B always felt like a small, immature and fearful child, and for the longest time I would judge myself and beat myself up (even more) for feeling this way. I didn't understand then what it so clear to me today – there is no wrong way to feel. My feelings are not wrong.

B would sabotage my goals and dreams and would get in the way of wanting to try new things or meet new people. B was a habitual over thinker, worry wart, people pleaser, judge and jury... suffice to say she was busy!

Understanding and learning to manage B is a daily exercise in mental and spiritual fitness! In the same way I brush my teeth and wash my hair, managing B is just as important so requires work! Constantly second guessing yourself is a full-time job. Here are 4 steps you can take to stop beating yourself up and learn to quieten, and show compassion to, your very own inner mean girl.

1. *Recognise your negative self-talk*

   You know when your friend says things like I feel so fat, I'm so bad at this, or I'll never get the promotion, your ears prickle and you immediately notice these negative and unhelpful things she is saying. Well, I need you to start to notice when you say the same types of things about yourself.

2. *Separate yourself from her by giving her a name*

   Giving your inner mean girl voice a name will help you separate yourself from and open a healthy dialogue with her. I want you to begin to talk to your inner mean girl voice very differently.

3. *Talk back using positive affirmations and kind and compassionate words*
   Remember your best friend who is in pain, or your daughter who fell? You would never tell her to shut up, call her a failure or stupid, so you please don't say it to yourself either. The goal is to turn the volume down on your inner mean girl voice, it is never to dismiss, judge or criticise her. She represents fear, pain, doubt and insecurity. In moments of suffering, we need love, kindness and a positive attitude. If you wouldn't say it to a friend, you shouldn't say it to yourself.

4. *Let her feel her feelings and then challenge her*
   Never beat her up, as she represents normal and natural feelings. Allow her time to feel and hold this space as a judgement and criticism free zone. When you have started to understand why your inner mean girl voice is feeling this way, you can compassionately remind her who is boss.

Positive affirmations play a crucial role in helping you to quieten your inner mean girl voice.

Positive affirmations are a proven method of self-improvement. They rewire our brains by targeting negative thoughts or beliefs and turning them into positives. All our inner dialogue and self-talk is a kind of affirmation and if repeated continually it will become a part of our life experiences and beliefs. So yes, affirmations can really work! But the chances are the affirmations, the internal chatter, you have been using up until now have been working against you and not for you!

To help you get started, on the page opposite I have listed some of the most common ways I observe women talk negatively to themselves. Next to these, I have given positive affirmations to swap them with. When deciding on which affirmation you would like to use it's important to pick something that still feels believable for you, otherwise you risk feeling worse about yourself if you fail to measure up. Chose an affirmation that takes you to just outside your comfort zone.

Negative self-talk	Positive Affirmation
I am a failure	There are no failures. I learn from everything I do
Everyone hates me	I love who I am and I love the person that I am becoming
Things never go well for me	I will never give up on myself
I'm not good enough	I love and accept myself unconditionally
I can't do it	I can do anything if I believe
I don't deserve it	My thoughts and opinions are valuable
I'm not pretty enough	I am enough, I am beautiful
I'm not smart enough	I am competent, smart and able
I'm stupid	I am always growing and developing
I'm fat	My body is strong and my happiness is not tied to how I look
I'm ugly	I am beautiful, I feel great about myself and my life
I'm a worthless	My life is filled with love, fun, friendship, all I have to do is stop all criticism, forgive, relax and be open
I'm useless	I have so much to give this world
No one would want me	I am loveable
I'll never be any good at it	I am courageous. I am willing to try
I hate myself	I love and accept myself exactly as I am now
I'll never get better at it	I am capable of achieving my goals
It's easy for her	I am happy she has achieved her goals, good for her!

"

If you wouldn't say it to your best friend, don't say it to yourself.

"

The Reframe-it Exercise

One of the most important lessons in self-esteem that I can teach you is to show you ways you can look for the gift in every challenge and the opportunities in every failure.

So many of us feel defeated and disheartened if we ever make a mistake, experience failure or have a setback. I want to show you how you can develop the mindset that every setback is an opportunity for a comeback...otherwise you will risk feeling worse about yourself.

Learning to overcome life's challenges will help you in more ways than one. You will become more resilient, confident and optimistic and this fabulous combination will help you to tackle more of what life throws at you. Instead of choosing to bury your head in the sand and wait for the problem to just go away, you will feel able to tackle it head on! Learning to reframe mistakes, failures and obstacles will have a very positive impact on your thoughts, feelings and actions.

On the page opposite, list the mistakes, challenges and failures you would like to turn around in your life. Then in the 'How Will I Reframe It?' column, write the step you will take to do so.

Mistakes, Failures and Obstacles	*How Will I Reframe It?*
For example: I applied for a job and I didn't get it.	For example: This was only one job I did not get. There are plenty more and I will apply for 3 more before the day is over.

Learning to Accept a Compliment

Learning to say thank you - choosing to say thank you and meaning it - after someone pays you a compliment is one of the super important lessons in self-love and acceptance that I can teach you. But why is it so hard to do? Selective perception is the tendency not to notice, or to quickly forget, things that contradict what we believe about ourselves. For example, maybe someone in work noticed that you got a haircut and complimented you on it. However, you hate the style and think you look awful so you struggle to accept this compliment. In some instances, you start to wonder if your colleague is lying to you.

Because you are your own toughest critic, it's hard to see the beauty, intelligence and kindness everyone else sees in you. But that doesn't mean it isn't there! So, how can you start to accept a compliment with grace... and mean it?

Next time someone gives you a compliment, quieten your inner mean girl voice and allow what they are saying to sink it. Wait a second before you respond, look into their eyes, smile and just say a simple thank you or try one of the following:

"Thanks, I appreciate that."

"Thank you, that's a really lovely thing to say."

"Thanks! That makes me feel good."

"Thanks! I like it too."

Even if you don't agree with the compliment, resist the urge to respond critically.

When you graciously accept a compliment, you are sharing a special connection and positive energy. Using the space provided on the opposite page start to record any compliments that you give and receive. This will help you to take stock and connect with the compliment. Do you notice any interesting patterns arise?

Space to reflect

Things that Make You Feel Beautiful

For women it can be quite challenging to overcome the extreme focus we may feel to look a certain way. We have been conditioned to think that our appearance is one of, if not the most, valuable part of ourselves. And the most desirable assets are youthful clear skin, being thin, white teeth and long hair (to name just a few). Many women base their identity on their body and only ever feel good if they look good physically. This is a sad and disturbing reality, affecting too many young girls and women.

Now it's time to change the way you think about beauty. Beauty comes in all different types, shapes, sizes, colours, ages and abilities. There are many ways to feel beautiful, both on the inside and on the outside. When thinking about your body image, it is important to factor in things you may not usually consider, such as a healthy digestive system, good eye sight or strong legs.

Using the opposite page, I want you to list five things that make you feel beautiful on the inside and the outside and five things that you appreciate about your body on the inside and the outside.

You can use this worksheet to help you combat bad body days, days when you are feeling self-conscious or when you feel under pressure to change your physical appearance.

Things that make me feel beautiful on the inside	Things that make me feel beautiful on the outside
For example: I am loving, thoughtful and compassionate to myself and others.	For example: My eyes, hair and hands make me feel beautiful.

Things that I appreciate about my body on the inside	Things that I appreciate about my body on the outside
For example: I appreciate my healthy digestive system, my memory and my sense of touch.	For example: I appreciate my legs, hips and bum.

“The problem is not your body and it has never been your body. You are, and always have been, beautiful. The problem is how you think about your body. Your body is not just a prop to express beauty. Your body is a vehicle to help you connect with movement, health, strength and power.”

Tips for Using Compassion in Everyday Life

If you wouldn't say it to your best friend, don't say it to yourself.

Can it really be that simple? Yes, it absolutely can. You can practice compassion with yourself and I hope that you will be surprised by how easy it is to do. Day 6 of this journal will be all you need to help you but I also wanted to give you just a little nudge in the right direction.

You are worthy of so much, but not just from other people! In your moments of pain, sadness and fear, imagine that it is your best friend, daughter, or mom in your shoes. Give yourself the same unconditional love and kindness that you would give them. Let us change the record together and use the following affirmation to remind us to always be our own best friend.

"I will treat myself with love, kindness, support and a positive attitude. I will treat myself as I would my best friend."

IRRESISTIBLE
NEGATIVITY
DELICIOUS
POSITIVITY

The 12-Week Journal

DATE ....

"I am confident"

WHAT DO YOU LIKE ABOUT WHO YOU ARE?

....

....

....

WHAT ARE SOME OF YOUR ACHIEVEMENTS?

....

....

....

WHAT QUALITIES HELPED YOU TO ACHIEVE THESE THINGS?

....

....

....

DATE ....

"I am fearless"

WHAT ARE SOME CHALLENGES THAT YOU HAVE OVERCOME TODAY?

WHICH OF YOUR QUALITIES HELPED YOU OVERCOME THESE CHALLENGES?

WHAT ARE YOUR UNIQUE SKILLS OR TALENTS?

DATE ....

"I am fabulous"

WHAT DO OTHER PEOPLE SAY THEY LIKE ABOUT YOU?

WHAT MAKES YOU SPECIAL?

HOW WOULD SOMEONE WHO CARES ABOUT YOU DESCRIBE YOU?

DATE ....

"I am fierce"

NOTE A TIME THAT YOU STOOD UP FOR YOURSELF

NOTE A TIME WHEN YOU FACED YOUR FEARS

DATE ....

"I am able & valuable"

NOTE ONE OR MORE OCCASIONS WHEN YOU HAVE OVERCOME ADVERSITY

LIST THREE PEOPLE YOU HAVE HELPED TODAY

LIST THREE THINGS YOU APPRECIATE ABOUT YOUR LIFE

DATE ....

"I am compassionate to myself"

WHAT WOULD YOU SAY TO SOMEONE YOU CARE ABOUT WHO WAS STRUGGLING WITH THE SAME ISSUE YOU ARE?

....

....

....

WHICH COMPASSIONATE AFFIRMATION ARE YOU COMFORTABLE SAYING TO YOURSELF WHEN YOU NEED SUPPORT?

....

....

....

WHAT ONE THING CAN YOU DO TODAY TO SHOW YOURSELF KINDNESS?

....

....

....

DATE ....

Weekly check-in

LIST THREE THINGS THAT HAPPENED THIS WEEK THAT YOU ARE GRATEFUL FOR

....

....

....

WHAT NEW THINGS DID YOU LEARN ABOUT YOURSELF THIS WEEK?

....

....

....

WHAT PLANS DO YOU HAVE NEXT WEEK THAT YOU FEEL EXCITED ABOUT?

....

....

....

Space to reflect

DATE ....

"I care for myself, my happiness & my wellbeing"

LIST THREE THINGS THAT HAPPENED TODAY THAT MADE YOU FEEL GRATEFUL

WHAT WAS YOUR GREATEST ACCOMPLISHMENT TODAY (IT DOESN'T MATTER HOW SMALL OR BIG)?

LIST THREE THINGS YOU LIKE ABOUT YOURSELF TODAY

DATE ....

"I have abundant energy & vitality"

WHAT MAKES YOUR HEART SING AND THE HAIRS ON THE BACK OF YOUR NECK STAND UP?

....

....

....

WHAT MAKES YOU FEEL ENERGETIC AND FULL OF VITALITY?

....

....

....

DATE ....

"I am courageous"

WHAT IS YOUR GREATEST FEAR IN LIFE RIGHT NOW?

WHAT IS THE ONE FEELING YOU'VE BEEN HAVING A HARD TIME TRYING TO UNDERSTAND?

WHAT IS A NEW HABIT YOU CAN ADOPT TO HELP YOU FEEL MORE CALM IN YOUR LIFE?

DATE ....

"I am unique"

WHAT IS WORTH SMILING ABOUT RIGHT NOW?

WHAT PARTS OF YOUR PERSONALITY MAKES YOU STAND OUT IN A POSITIVE WAY?

WHAT ARE YOUR UNIQUE SKILLS OR TALENTS?

DATE ....

"I am happy"

I FELT HAPPIEST WHEN I...

I HAD FUN WHEN I...

I MADE MYSELF PROUD WHEN I...

DATE ....

"I am compassionate to myself"

WHAT WOULD YOU SAY TO SOMEONE YOU CARE ABOUT WHO WAS STRUGGLING WITH THE SAME ISSUE YOU ARE?

....

....

....

WHICH COMPASSIONATE AFFIRMATION ARE YOU COMFORTABLE SAYING TO YOURSELF WHEN YOU NEED SUPPORT?

....

....

....

WHAT ONE THING CAN YOU DO TODAY TO SHOW YOURSELF KINDNESS?

....

....

....

DATE ....

Weekly check-in

LIST THREE THINGS THAT HAPPENED THIS WEEK THAT YOU ARE GRATEFUL FOR

....

....

....

WHAT NEW THINGS DID YOU LEARN ABOUT YOURSELF THIS WEEK?

....

....

....

WHAT PLANS DO YOU HAVE NEXT WEEK THAT YOU FEEL EXCITED ABOUT?

....

....

....

Space to reflect

DATE ....

"I am worthy"

WHEN DO YOU FEEL BAD ABOUT YOURSELF AND WHY?

WHAT WAS YOUR GREATEST ACCOMPLISHMENT TODAY?

DATE ....

"I am worthy of love"

WHAT ARE YOUR BEST OR FAVOURITE QUALITIES?

WHAT MAKES YOU FEEL LOVED?

WHO ARE THE PEOPLE IN YOUR LIFE WHO ARE NON-JUDGMENTAL AND GENUINELY HAVE YOUR HEART IN MIND?

DATE ....

"I am loving"

IF YOU LOVED YOURSELF MORE FULLY, HOW WOULD YOU TREAT YOURSELF EVERY DAY?

....

....

....

WHAT'S ONE SMALL WAY YOU CAN START DOING THAT TODAY?

....

....

....

DATE ....

"I am motivated and determined to achieve my goals"

WHAT ARE YOUR GOALS?

....

....

....

AS A FIRST STEP, WHAT CAN YOU DO TODAY TO HELP YOU TO ACHIEVE YOUR GOALS?

....

....

....

DATE ....

"I am considerate to myself"

HOW CAN YOU BE A NURTURING FRIEND TO YOURSELF?

WHAT STEPS CAN YOU TAKE TO ENSURE YOU ARE CONSIDERATE TO YOURSELF TODAY?

DATE ....

"I am compassionate to myself"

WHAT WOULD YOU SAY TO SOMEONE YOU CARE ABOUT WHO WAS STRUGGLING WITH THE SAME ISSUE YOU ARE?

....

....

....

WHICH COMPASSIONATE AFFIRMATION ARE YOU COMFORTABLE SAYING TO YOURSELF WHEN YOU NEED SUPPORT?

....

....

....

WHAT ONE THING CAN YOU DO TODAY TO SHOW YOURSELF KINDNESS?

....

....

....

DATE ....

Weekly check-in

LIST THREE THINGS THAT HAPPENED THIS WEEK THAT YOU ARE GRATEFUL FOR

....

....

....

WHAT NEW THINGS DID YOU LEARN ABOUT YOURSELF THIS WEEK?

....

....

....

WHAT PLANS DO YOU HAVE NEXT WEEK THAT YOU FEEL EXCITED ABOUT?

....

....

....

Space to reflect

DATE ....

"I am friendly"

WHO IS YOUR CLOSEST FRIEND?

....

....

....

WHAT TYPE OF FRIEND DO YOU WANT TO BE?

....

....

....

DATE ....

"I am kind"

WHAT IS PREVENTING YOU FROM BEING KIND TO YOURSELF?

WHAT'S ONE SMALL STEP CAN YOU TAKE TO START TO BE KIND TO YOURSELF?

WHAT IS ONE HEALTHY THING YOU CAN DO TO SUPPORT YOURSELF WHEN YOU ARE SAD OR STRESSED OUT?

DATE ....

"I am strong"

WHEN DO YOU FEEL POSITIVE ABOUT YOURSELF?

WHAT MAKES YOU FEEL STRONG?

DATE ....

"I am affectionate"

WHAT EVENT REGULARLY REPLAYS IN YOUR HEAD AND MAKES YOU UNHAPPY?

....

....

....

HOW CAN YOU SHOW YOURSELF COMPASSION WHEN YOU THINK ABOUT THIS EVENT?

....

....

....

DATE ....

"I am adventurous"

WHAT DO YOU WISH THAT YOU COULD DO?

....

....

....

WHAT IS HOLDING YOU BACK FROM DOING IT?

....

....

....

DATE ....

"I am compassionate to myself"

WHAT WOULD YOU SAY TO SOMEONE YOU CARE ABOUT WHO WAS STRUGGLING WITH THE SAME ISSUE YOU ARE?

....

....

....

WHICH COMPASSIONATE AFFIRMATION ARE YOU COMFORTABLE SAYING TO YOURSELF WHEN YOU NEED SUPPORT?

....

....

....

WHAT ONE THING CAN YOU DO TODAY TO SHOW YOURSELF KINDNESS?

....

....

....

DATE ....

Weekly check-in

LIST THREE THINGS THAT HAPPENED THIS WEEK THAT YOU ARE GRATEFUL FOR

WHAT NEW THINGS DID YOU LEARN ABOUT YOURSELF THIS WEEK?

WHAT PLANS DO YOU HAVE NEXT WEEK THAT YOU FEEL EXCITED ABOUT?

“

I accept the woman that I already am. I feel gratitude and appreciation for all the things in my life that have made me who I am today.

”

DATE ....

"I am healthy"

WHAT IS ONE HEALTHY THING YOU CAN DO TO SUPPORT YOURSELF WHEN YOU ARE SAD OR STRESSED OUT?

WHAT PHYSICAL ACTIVITIES DO YOU ACTUALLY ENJOY?

WHICH FOODS MAKE YOU FEEL HEALTHY, VIBRANT AND ENERGISED?

DATE ....

"I am beautiful"

WHEN DO YOU FEEL BEAUTIFUL?

WHAT IS YOUR FAVOURITE PHYSICAL FEATURE AND WHY DO YOU LOVE THIS PART OF YOU?

BEAUTY COMES FROM WITHIN. WHAT ONE THING MAKES YOU FEEL BEAUTIFUL ON THE INSIDE?

DATE ....

"My body is strong"

WHAT MAKES YOU FEEL STRONG?

....

....

....

MAKE A LIST OF THINGS THAT YOUR BODY CAN DO. FOR EXAMPLE, RUN, CYCLE, CLIMB MOUNTAINS

....

....

....

DATE ....

"I am grateful to my body"

LIST THREE THINGS THAT YOU ARE GRATEFUL YOUR BODY CAN DO

HOW HAS YOUR BODY HELPED YOU AND SUPPORTED YOU TODAY OR IN YOUR LIFE?

DATE ....

"I am vibrant"

HOW MUCH SLEEP DO YOU NEED?

WHAT STRESSES YOU OUT?

WHAT RELAXES YOU?

DATE ....

"I am compassionate to myself"

WHAT WOULD YOU SAY TO SOMEONE YOU CARE ABOUT WHO WAS STRUGGLING WITH THE SAME ISSUE YOU ARE?

WHICH COMPASSIONATE AFFIRMATION ARE YOU COMFORTABLE SAYING TO YOURSELF WHEN YOU NEED SUPPORT?

WHAT ONE THING CAN YOU DO TODAY TO SHOW YOURSELF KINDNESS?

DATE ....

Weekly check-in

LIST THREE THINGS THAT HAPPENED THIS WEEK THAT YOU ARE GRATEFUL FOR

WHAT NEW THINGS DID YOU LEARN ABOUT YOURSELF THIS WEEK?

WHAT PLANS DO YOU HAVE NEXT WEEK THAT YOU FEEL EXCITED ABOUT?

Space to reflect

DATE ....

"I am passionate"

WHAT MAKES YOU SAD?

....

....

....

WHAT MAKES YOU HAPPY?

....

....

....

WHAT MAKES YOU ANGRY?

....

....

....

DATE ....

"I am self-driven"

WHAT TYPE OF PERSON DO YOU WANT TO BE?
LIST THREE WORDS.

WHAT TYPE OF FRIEND DO YOU WANT TO BE?
LIST THREE WORDS.

WHAT DO YOU THINK ABOUT YOURSELF TODAY?

DATE ....

"I am full of life"

WHAT THINGS DO YOU VALUE IN LIFE?

WHAT MAKES YOU AFRAID?

WHAT DID YOU SEE BEAUTY IN TODAY?

DATE ....

"I am resilient"

WHEN DO YOU FEEL BAD ABOUT YOURSELF?

....

....

....

HOW DO YOU BOUNCE BACK FROM FEELING BAD?

....

....

....

DATE ....

"I am perceptive"

WHAT IS THE MOST IMPORTANT THING IN YOUR LIFE?

WHO ARE THE MOST IMPORTANT PEOPLE IN YOUR LIFE?

WHAT CAN YOU DO TODAY TO BE GRATEFUL AND APPRECIATIVE TO THESE THINGS AND PEOPLE?

DATE ....

"I am compassionate to myself"

WHAT WOULD YOU SAY TO SOMEONE YOU CARE ABOUT WHO WAS STRUGGLING WITH THE SAME ISSUE YOU ARE?

....

....

....

WHICH COMPASSIONATE AFFIRMATION ARE YOU COMFORTABLE SAYING TO YOURSELF WHEN YOU NEED SUPPORT?

....

....

....

WHAT ONE THING CAN YOU DO TODAY TO SHOW YOURSELF KINDNESS?

....

....

....

DATE ....

Weekly check-in

LIST THREE THINGS THAT HAPPENED THIS WEEK THAT YOU ARE GRATEFUL FOR

WHAT NEW THINGS DID YOU LEARN ABOUT YOURSELF THIS WEEK?

WHAT PLANS DO YOU HAVE NEXT WEEK THAT YOU FEEL EXCITED ABOUT?

Space to reflect

DATE ....

"I am successful"

WHAT DOES SUCCESS MEAN TO YOU?

WHAT DO YOU BELIEVE A SUCCESSFUL PERSON MUST DO IN ORDER TO BE SUCCESSFUL?

DATE ....

"I can & I will achieve my goals"

WHAT IS YOUR BIGGEST GOAL IN LIFE RIGHT NOW?

....

....

....

WHY IS THIS GOAL IMPORTANT TO YOU?

....

....

....

WHAT DO YOU NEED TO DO TO MAKE THIS GOAL A REALITY?

....

....

....

DATE ....

"I am positive"

LIST THREE POSITIVE THINGS THAT HAPPENED TO YOU TODAY

....

....

....

LIST THREE THINGS YOU DID TO HELP SOMEONE FEEL POSITIVE ABOUT THEIR DAY

....

....

....

HOW DID YOU OVERCOME A PROBLEM TODAY?

....

....

....

DATE ....

"I am enough"

LIST THREE THINGS THAT MADE YOU FEEL ENOUGH TODAY

WHEN DID YOU FEEL EMPOWERED TODAY?

DATE ....

"I like myself"

WHAT IS YOUR FAVOURITE PERSONAL QUALITY?

WHAT THREE THINGS MAKE YOU UNIQUE?

WHAT WAS THE BEST PART OF TODAY?

DATE ....

"I am compassionate to myself"

WHAT WOULD YOU SAY TO SOMEONE YOU CARE ABOUT WHO WAS STRUGGLING WITH THE SAME ISSUE YOU ARE?

WHICH COMPASSIONATE AFFIRMATION ARE YOU COMFORTABLE SAYING TO YOURSELF WHEN YOU NEED SUPPORT?

WHAT ONE THING CAN YOU DO TODAY TO SHOW YOURSELF KINDNESS?

DATE ....

Weekly check-in

LIST THREE THINGS THAT HAPPENED THIS WEEK THAT YOU ARE GRATEFUL FOR

....

....

....

WHAT NEW THINGS DID YOU LEARN ABOUT YOURSELF THIS WEEK?

....

....

....

WHAT PLANS DO YOU HAVE NEXT WEEK THAT YOU FEEL EXCITED ABOUT?

....

....

....

Space to reflect

DATE ....

"I am confident"

WHAT DO YOU LIKE ABOUT WHO YOU ARE?

WHAT ARE SOME OF YOUR ACHIEVEMENTS?

WHAT QUALITIES HELPED YOU TO ACHIEVE THESE THINGS?

DATE ....

"I am important"

IF YOU WERE TO WRITE TO YOUR YOUNGER SELF, WHAT AGE WOULD YOU CHOOSE?

IF YOU COULD TELL YOUR PAST SELF ONE THING THAT YOU KNOW NOW, WHAT WOULD IT BE?

DATE ....

"I deserve the same care I give to others"

HOW WOULD YOU CARE FOR SOMEONE WHO IS HAVING A DIFFICULT DAY?

....

....

....

WHAT DID YOU DO TODAY THAT MADE YOU FEEL GOOD ABOUT YOURSELF?

....

....

....

DATE ....

"I am sexy"

SEXY IS AN ATTITUDE. WHAT MAKES YOU FEEL SEXY?

....

....

....

IF YOU LOVED YOURSELF MORE FULLY, HOW WOULD YOU TREAT YOURSELF EVERY DAY?

....

....

....

DATE ....

"I am in charge of my own mind"

WHAT HAPPENED TODAY, OR IN YOUR LIFE, THAT YOU TOOK PERSONALLY?

....

....

....

HOW MIGHT YOU REPSOND TO THESE CIRCUMSTANACES DIFFERENTLY IN THE FUTURE?

....

....

....

DATE ....

"I am compassionate to myself"

WHAT WOULD YOU SAY TO SOMEONE YOU CARE ABOUT WHO WAS STRUGGLING WITH THE SAME ISSUE YOU ARE?

WHICH COMPASSIONATE AFFIRMATION ARE YOU COMFORTABLE SAYING TO YOURSELF WHEN YOU NEED SUPPORT?

WHAT ONE THING CAN YOU DO TODAY TO SHOW YOURSELF KINDNESS?

DATE ....

Weekly check-in

THREE THINGS THAT HAPPENED THIS WEEK THAT I AM GRATEFUL FOR

WHAT NEW THINGS DID I LEARN ABOUT MYSELF THIS WEEK

WHAT PLANS DO I HAVE NEXT WEEK THAT I FEEL EXCITED ABOUT?

"

Self-esteem will be the bricks we use to rebuild your relationship to yourself, but self-compassion will be the cement holding it all together.

"

DATE ....

"I am motivated"

GIVE YOURSELF A GOAL FOR THIS WEEK

....

....

....

WHAT ARE YOUR REASONS FOR WANTING TO ACHIEVE YOUR GOAL?

....

....

....

WHAT STEPS DO YOU NEED TO TAKE TO MOVE CLOSER TO YOUR GOAL?

....

....

....

DATE ....

"I am bright"

WHAT DO YOU LIKE ABOUT YOURSELF TODAY?

....

....

....

WHAT COULD YOU DO TODAY TO SHARE YOUR BRIGHTNESS WITH OTHERS?

....

....

....

DATE ....

"I can overcome my problems"

WHETHER MAJOR OR MINOR, NOTE A TIME THAT YOU FACED A PROBLEM TODAY

....

....

....

LIST SOMEONE WHO HAS HELPED YOU TO OVERCOME A PROBLEM TODAY

....

....

....

DATE ....

"My life is good"

LIST THREE THINGS THAT MADE YOU SMILE TODAY

WHAT WAS THE BEST PART OF TODAY?

WHAT CAN YOU DO TOMORROW TO BUILD ON TODAY'S SUCCESS?

DATE ....

"I am human, we all make mistakes"

HOW CAN YOU USE A PAST MISTAKE TO IMPROVE YOUR SITUATION?

....

....

....

HAVE YOU PUT IN THE EFFORT TO ACHIEVE A RESULT YOU ARE PROUD OF?

....

....

....

LIST THREE THINGS THAT YOU APPRECIATE ABOUT YOUR LIFE RIGHT NOW

....

....

....

DATE ....

"I am compassionate to myself"

WHAT WOULD YOU SAY TO SOMEONE YOU CARE ABOUT WHO WAS STRUGGLING WITH THE SAME ISSUE YOU ARE?

....

....

....

WHICH COMPASSIONATE AFFIRMATION ARE YOU COMFORTABLE SAYING TO YOURSELF WHEN YOU NEED SUPPORT?

....

....

....

WHAT ONE THING CAN YOU DO TODAY TO SHOW YOURSELF KINDNESS?

....

....

....

DATE ....

Weekly check-in

LIST THREE THINGS THAT HAPPENED THIS WEEK THAT YOU ARE GRATEFUL FOR

WHAT NEW THINGS DID YOU LEARN ABOUT YOURSELF THIS WEEK?

WHAT PLANS DO YOU HAVE NEXT WEEK THAT YOU FEEL EXCITED ABOUT?

Space to reflect

DATE ....

"I am always learning"

HOW DID YOU TACKLE THE BIGGEST CHALLENGE YOU FACED TODAY?

WHAT CAN YOU GET BETTER AT BY PRACTICING?

DATE ....

"I look for opportunities"

WHAT OPPORTUNITIES HAVE YOU TAKEN ADVANTAGE OF TODAY OR IN YOUR LIFE?

ARE YOU PROUD OF ANY WORK YOU HAVE COMPLETED TODAY OR IN LIFE? WHY OR WHY NOT?

DATE ....

"I believe I am worthy of achieving my goals"

HOW DOES RECEIVING FEEDBACK (GOOD OR BAD) MAKE YOU FEEL ABOUT YOURSELF?

....

....

....

THE NEXT TIME YOU HAVE A SETBACK HOW COULD YOU REACT DIFFERENTLY?

....

....

....

DATE ....

"I am gentle"

HOW CAN YOU BE GENTLE WITH YOURSELF TODAY?

HOW CAN YOU GIVE YOURSELF ENCOURAGEMENT TODAY?

HOW CAN YOU FIND 10 MINUTES FOR YOURSELF TO BE MINDFUL AND PRESENT?

DATE ....

"I am discovering how wonderful I am"

WHAT DID YOU LEARN ABOUT YOURSELF TODAY?

WHAT MADE YOU LAUGH TODAY?

WHAT MADE YOU FEEL CONTENT TODAY?

DATE ....

"I am compassionate to myself"

WHAT WOULD YOU SAY TO SOMEONE YOU CARE ABOUT WHO WAS STRUGGLING WITH THE SAME ISSUE YOU ARE?

WHICH COMPASSIONATE AFFIRMATION ARE YOU COMFORTABLE SAYING TO YOURSELF WHEN YOU NEED SUPPORT?

WHAT ONE THING CAN YOU DO TODAY TO SHOW YOURSELF KINDNESS?

DATE ....

Weekly check-in

LIST THREE THINGS THAT HAPPENED THIS WEEK THAT YOU ARE GRATEFUL FOR

WHAT NEW THINGS DID YOU LEARN ABOUT YOURSELF THIS WEEK?

WHAT PLANS DO YOU HAVE NEXT WEEK THAT YOU FEEL EXCITED ABOUT?

Space to reflect

DATE ....

"I am proud of myself"

HOW DID YOU MAKE YOURSELF FEEL PROUD TODAY?

....

....

....

WHAT EMPOWERED YOU TODAY?

....

....

....

DATE ....

"I say yes to myself"

LIST THREE TIMES YOU SAID NO TO YOURSELF

....

....

....

WHY DID YOU SAY NO TO YOURSELF?

....

....

....

SOMETIMES SAYING YES TO YOURSELF MEANS SAYING NO TO OTHERS. HOW DID YOU SAY NO TO OTHERS TODAY?

....

....

....

DATE ....

"I am worthy of all the happiness that I create"

WHAT WAS THE BEST PART OF YOUR DAY TODAY?

DATE ....

"I am calm"

LIST THREE THINGS THAT YOU SAW TODAY THAT MADE YOU FEEL POSITIVE

....

....

....

LIST THREE THINGS THAT BROUGHT YOU A SENSE OF PEACE AND CALM

....

....

....

DATE ....

"I am powerful"

WHAT MADE YOU FEEL BAD ABOUT YOURSELF TODAY?

HOW DID YOU USE YOUR INNER-POWER TO OVERCOME YOUR NEGATIVE THOUGHTS?

DATE ....

"I am compassionate to myself"

WHAT WOULD YOU SAY TO SOMEONE YOU CARE ABOUT WHO WAS STRUGGLING WITH THE SAME ISSUE YOU ARE?

....

....

....

WHICH COMPASSIONATE AFFIRMATION ARE YOU COMFORTABLE SAYING TO YOURSELF WHEN YOU NEED SUPPORT?

....

....

....

WHAT ONE THING CAN YOU DO TODAY TO SHOW YOURSELF KINDNESS?

....

....

....

DATE ....

Weekly check-in

LIST THREE THINGS THAT HAPPENED THIS WEEK THAT YOU ARE GRATEFUL FOR

WHAT NEW THINGS DID YOU LEARN ABOUT YOURSELF THIS WEEK?

WHAT PLANS DO YOU HAVE NEXT WEEK THAT YOU FEEL EXCITED ABOUT?

Space to reflect

DATE ....

"I achieve great things"

WHAT DO YOU LIKE ABOUT WHO YOU ARE?

WHAT CHARACTERISTICS DO YOU HAVE THAT ARE POSITIVE?

DATE ....

"I am in control of my life"

WHAT CHALLENGES HAVE YOU OVERCOME TODAY?

WHICH OF YOUR QUALITIES HELPED YOU OVERCOME THESE CHALLENGES?

DATE ....

"I am patient with myself"

WHAT IS YOU BIGGEST PAIN IN LIFE RIGHT NOW?

WHAT CAN YOU DO TO START HEALING THIS PAIN?

DATE ....

"I am able to forgive"

LIST THREE OCCASIONS WHERE YOU HAVE OVERCOME ADVERSITY IN YOUR LIFE

....

....

....

LIST THREE THINGS YOU APPRECIATE ABOUT YOUR LIFE

....

....

....

DATE ....

"I am my own best friend"

DESCRIBE A TIME WHEN YOU TREATED YOURSELF LIKE YOU WOULD TREAT YOUR BEST FRIEND

HOW HAVE YOU GROWN AS A PERSON SINCE YOU STARTED THIS JOURNEY TO BECOME YOUR OWN BEST FRIEND?

DATE ....

"I am compassionate to myself"

WHAT WOULD YOU SAY TO SOMEONE YOU CARE ABOUT WHO WAS STRUGGLING WITH THE SAME ISSUE YOU ARE?

....

....

....

WHICH COMPASSIONATE AFFIRMATION ARE YOU COMFORTABLE SAYING TO YOURSELF WHEN YOU NEED SUPPORT?

....

....

....

WHAT ONE THING CAN YOU DO TODAY TO SHOW YOURSELF KINDNESS?

....

....

....

DATE ....

Weekly check-in

LIST THREE THINGS THAT HAPPENED THIS WEEK THAT YOU ARE GRATEFUL FOR

WHAT NEW THINGS DID YOU LEARN ABOUT YOURSELF THIS WEEK?

WHAT PLANS DO YOU HAVE NEXT WEEK THAT YOU FEEL EXCITED ABOUT?

BEST
FRIEND

Congratulations ...you are fabulous!

But you have always been fabulous and I hope this journal has helped you to see that. One of the best things you can do now is to grab a glass of wine or a cup of tea, put your feet up and take a look back over the journal to see how far you have come. Take stock of all you have learned about yourself and smile. You are incredible, simply because you are you!

Acknowledgements

My world as a life coach would not exist if it wasn't for my love, James. I am forever grateful to you for giving me my wings and helping me to fly.

Thank you to my amazing family. Kate, for helping me with L-School and Emma for dotting the i's and crossing the t's. You guys are two of the best things I have in my life. Right side. Thank you to my mom for being my rock and my inspiration. Thanks to dad for your advice and support as I tread often very unfamiliar territory as a self-employed person.

Thank you to Juliette for always getting excited about my work.

Thank you to Kelly for helping to give this journal a name and to the team at White Bear Studios (Buzz and Esme) for designing the cover and breathing life into my dream.

Thank you to my project manager Becca for the deadlines, encouragement and support. We only knew each other for a short time before we started working together but you always had my best interests at heart.

Thanks to Lisa who created the beautiful illustrations you see in this book. Three days before my final deadline you created two incredible illustrations that beautifully captured the journey I hope this book has taken everyone on. You can find more of her incredible work on her @sheddrawsanything

Thanks to B. I know your pain was real and fear was sometimes overwhelming but I listened to you, I always listened. And together we walked hand in hand to make our dreams come true. We did it. I am so proud.

Writing this journal was one of the scariest things I have ever done. Thank you for investing in this book, and in turn investing in yourself. I am so grateful and honoured that you have decided to join me on this journey and I hope this book helps you find compassion, love and kindness.

From the bottom of my heart I want to thank you for being a part of my journey to becoming my own best friend.

Here's to you, you are worth it!

Sarah x

About the Author

Sarah is a life coach, a speaker, the creator of an online learning community called L-School and the founder of The Better Life Project, her life coaching business for women. She works with women all over the world to help them achieve their personal and professional goals, whilst developing their confidence and self-esteem. Since setting up The Better Life Project, Sarah has presented at a TedX conference, won multiple business awards and created one of Ireland's most unique and transformative workshops exclusively for women called The Empowered Women Workshop.

Say hello to Sarah:

- f TheBetterLifeProjectIreland
- SarahDoyleBLP
- Sarah_thebetterlifeproject

notes

notes

notes